D0837744

It's Magic?

by Robert Lopshire

SCHOLASTIC BOOK SERVICES

NEW YORK • TORONTO • LONDON • AUCKLAND • SYDNEY

This book is sold subject to the condition that it shall not be resold, lent, or otherwise circulated in any binding or cover other than that in which it is published — unless prior written permission has been obtained from the publisher — and without a similar condition, including this condition, being imposed on the subsequent purchaser.

Copyright © 1969 by Robert Lopshire. This edition is published by Scholastic Book Services, a division of Scholastic Magazines, Inc., by arrangement with The Macmillan Company.

4th printing .... August 1970

Printed in the U.S.A.

"I like magic!" said Boris.
"Come right in," said Tad.

The Magic Star

For his first trick,
Tad got a dish,
some water,
and five toothpicks.

Tad bent the toothpicks.
He did not break them.
He put them in the dish.

Tad got the water.
"This is magic water, Boris!
Put some on the toothpicks!"

Boris did it.

The toothpicks moved.
In two minutes they made a star!
"Wow!" said Boris.
"That sure is magic water!"
"Yes," said Tad.
"It seems to be."

The Take Away Trick

Tad got a newspaper and a can.
He asked Boris
to take away the newspaper
without touching the can.

"That is easy!" said Boris.
"I will just pull hard
on the newspaper!"

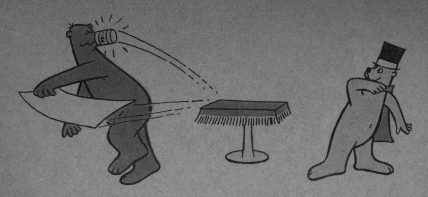

"Ouch!" said Boris.

"I must have done something wrong!"

Then Tad did it.

He rolled the newspaper.

He did not touch the can.

The paper pushed on the can.

The can stayed on the table.

"I did not think of that," said Boris.

The Water Trick

Tad got a glass of water
and a napkin.

Tad put the napkin
over the glass.
"I will drink the water,"
he said.
"But I will not
take off the napkin to do it.

"Ka-Voom!" said Tad.
"The water is gone!"

"Ha!" said Boris.
"It is not gone!"

"It is now," said Tad.
"And I did not take off
the napkin.
You did!"

The Napkin Trick

Tad got three paper napkins.
Two white and one colored.
He tied the white ones together.

"Now, Boris, see if you can
put the colored napkin
between the white napkins.
You cannot tear them.
You cannot untie the knot."

"If I cannot tear them
or untie them," said Boris,
"it cannot be done!"

"All you have to do is this," said Tad.
"Now the colored one
is between the white ones!"
"You fooled me again!" said Boris.

The Jump Trick

Tad got a penny.

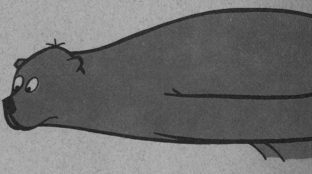

Tad rubbed the penny.
"Flooby-Dooby!" he said.
"Now it is a magic penny."
"Really?" asked Boris.
"Really," said Tad.

"If I put my magic penny down,
you cannot jump over it," said Tad.
"I bet I can!" said Boris.

Tad put the penny
on Boris' head.
"Go on," he said.
"Jump over the penny."
"You tricked me!" said Boris.
"I know it," said Tad.

The Magic Clips

Tad got a piece of paper
and two paper clips.

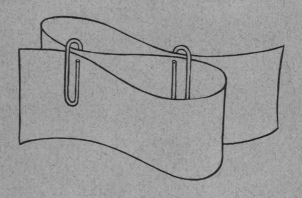

He bent the paper around.
He put the paper clips
on the paper like this.
He gave the paper to Boris.

"I will say magic words," said Tad.
"When I do,
pull the ends of the paper.
Pull hard!

"Rip-Zip-Flip-Clip!" said Tad.
Boris pulled.

"The clips are together!"
said Boris.
"That is real magic!"
"Anyone can do it," said Tad,
"if they say, 'Rip-Zip-Flip-Clip!'"

It's Knot Magic

Tad got a handkerchief.
He rolled it up.

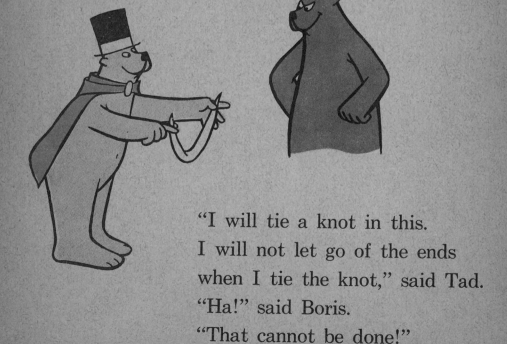

"I will tie a knot in this.
I will not let go of the ends
when I tie the knot," said Tad.
"Ha!" said Boris.
"That cannot be done!"

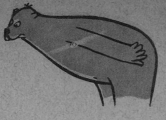

Tad put the handkerchief
on the table.
He crossed his arms
and picked up the ends.

Tad held the ends tight.
He pulled his arms apart.
There was the knot!
"Oh!" said Boris. "I can do that!"

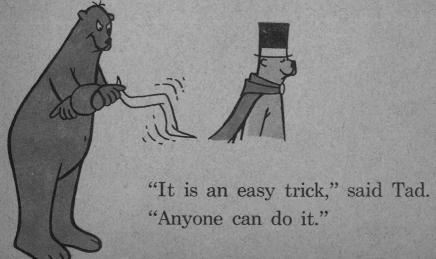

"It is an easy trick," said Tad.
"Anyone can do it."

A Paper Trick

"I will make this paper
hold this book up in the air,"
said Tad.

"There must be a trick to it,"
said Boris.
"You are right!" said Tad.

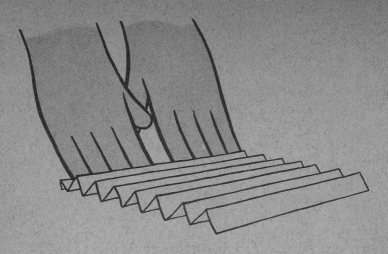

Tad folded the paper like this.

He stood the paper
on the table.
He put the book on the paper.
"There!" said Tad.
"I like that!" said Boris.

A Tough Egg

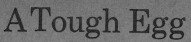

"Hold your hands
like this," said Tad.
Boris did it.

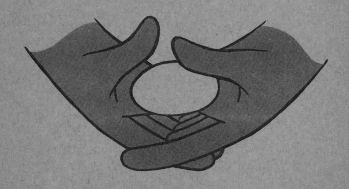

Tad put an egg
in Boris' hands.
He put it this way.

"Squeeze!" said Tad.
"Try to break the egg!"
Boris squeezed the egg
as hard as he could.
"It won't break!" he said.
"That's right," said Tad.
"No one can break an egg
by squeezing it that way!"

When you do this trick,
use a hard-boiled egg.

The Card Drop

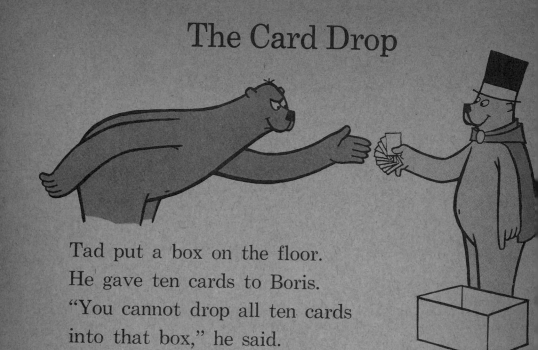

Tad put a box on the floor.
He gave ten cards to Boris.
"You cannot drop all ten cards
into that box," he said.
"Ho! Ho!" laughed Boris.
"This will be easy!"

Boris took aim.
He dropped the cards.
Only two went in the box.
"It must be that box!"
said Boris.

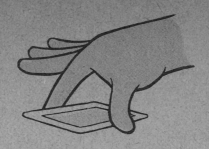

"It is not the box," said Tad.
He held the cards like this.

He let them drop flat.
Every card went in the box.
"I knew it all the time,"
said Boris.

The Magic Straw

Tad got a bottle and a straw.

"Pick up the bottle
with the straw," said Tad.
"You must not touch the bottle
with your hands."

Boris could not do it.

Tad bent the straw.
He put it in the bottle.
He picked the bottle up.
"I knew it all the time,"
said Boris.

The Magic Word

"For my next trick," said Tad,
"I will use one magic word."

"When I say the magic word
you will not be able to keep
your foot up like this!"
"Ha!" said Boris.
"I bet I can!"

"Put your right foot
against the wall," said Tad.
"I will now say the magic word.
BLOOKUS!
Try to hold up your left foot!"

"I cannot lift my foot!" said Boris.
"Blookus is a very magic word,"
said Tad.
"It sure is!" said Boris.

The Magic Picture

Tad put some lemon juice in a dish.

Tad got some white paper.
He put a toothpick in the juice.
He drew a picture.
He used a lot of juice.

When the picture was dry,
there was nothing on the paper!

Then he held the paper
against a light bulb.
It was a big bulb.

"Now clap your hands," said Tad,
"and say 'Boris' five times."

Tad gave the paper to Boris.
There was a picture!
"A good trick," said Boris.
"But it is not very funny!"

The Crazy Paper

Tad made two tears
in a piece of paper.

He asked Boris to tear
both ends away from the middle
in one tear.
"Now I have you!" said Boris.
"This will be easy!"

Boris tried and tried.
But only one piece would tear off.

"I give up," said Boris.
"How do you do it?"

"Like this," said Tad.

Tad said, "I think this
is the end of the magic show."